Become a SATs star with CGP!

This CGP SAT Buster is perfect for helping pupils prepare for the Reasoning SATs test. It's packed with fun and friendly questions to help them develop every skill they'll need.

It also includes self-assessment tick boxes so that pupils can make a note of how confident they feel about each topic — ideal for keeping track of their progress.

What CGP is all about

Our sole aim here at CGP is to produce the highest quality books — carefully written, immaculately presented and dangerously close to being funny.

Then we work our socks off to get them out to you — at the cheapest possible prices.

Contents

Published by CGP

Editors: Izzy Bowen, Emma Cleasby and Ruth Wilbourne

With thanks to Alan Jones and Karen Wells for the proofreading.
Also thanks to Jan Greenway for the copyright research.

Coin images on pages 32 and 33 © iStock.com

ISBN: 978 1 78294 713 4

Clipart from Corel®
Printed by Elanders Ltd, Newcastle upon Tyne.
Based on the classic CGP style created by Richard Parsons.

Numbers 1 to 20

1. Draw lines to match each number to the correct word.
   One has been done for you.

Thirteen

1

Eight   8

Eighteen

18

One

13

2. Write each number in words.

11   eleven

17   Seaven teen

3. Fill in the missing numbers on these shirts.

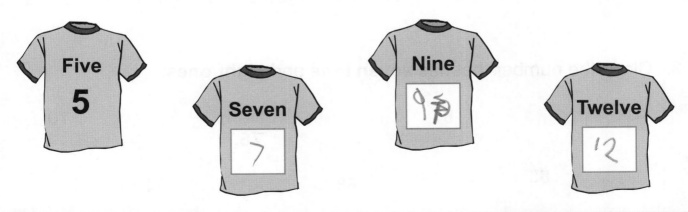

Five
5

Seven
7

Nine
9 ~~P~~

Twelve
12

Are you bouncing like a Reasoning Roo? ✓ ✓ ✓

Place Value

1. Draw lines to match each number with the
   group of **tens** and **ones** it is made up of.

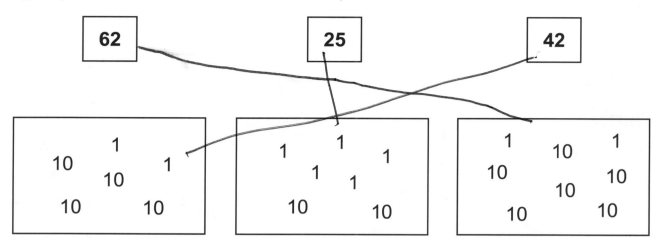

| 62 | 25 | 42 |

| 10 1 1 10 10 10 | 1 1 1 1 1 10 10 | 1 10 1 10 10 10 10 |

2. Jamal has **3** bags of carrots and **2** potatoes.
   Each bag has **10** carrots inside it.

How many vegetables does Jamal have in total?

vegetables

3. Circle the number that has **seven tens** and **eight ones**.

71   87   70

                                        78

        83   68   81

Numbers as Words

1. Write each number in words.

22   *twentytwo*

85   *805*

2. Draw lines to match each number with the correct word.

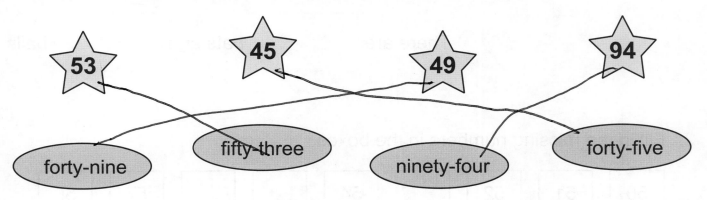

53   45   49   94

forty-nine   fifty-three   ninety-four   forty-five

3. Write these words as numbers.

ninety-nine   thirty-eight *83*   sixty-four

4. Each person's age is written below them. They all have a birthday balloon.
   Circle the person who has the **wrong** balloon.

11   61   32   13

eleven   sixty-one   fifty-two   thirteen

Are you jumping like a Reasoning Roo?

    Section 1 — Numbers

Counting

1. How many **bats** and **balls** are there in the picture below?

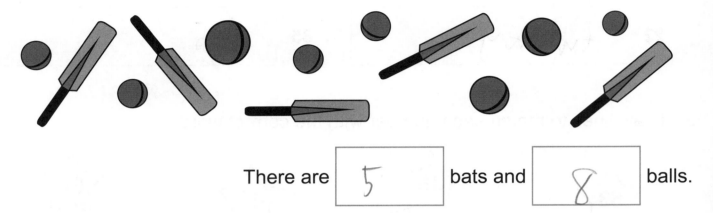

There are [5] bats and [8] balls.

2. Fill in the missing numbers in the boxes.

| 50 | 51 | 52 | 53 | 54 | 55 | 56 | 57 | 58 |

3. Colour in **13** tomatoes.

4. Fill in the missing numbers.

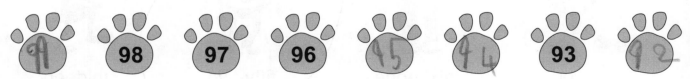

99   98   97   96   95   94   93   92

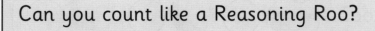
Can you count like a Reasoning Roo?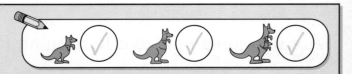

Counting in 2s, 3s, 5s and 10s

1. Fill in the next three numbers in this pattern.

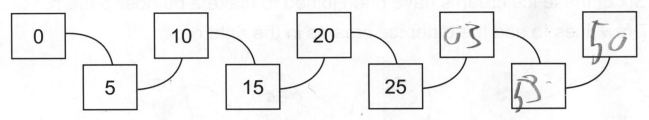

0		10		20		03		50
	5		15		25		53	

2. Write the next three numbers in this pattern.

2   4   6   8   10   12   14

3. Fill in the missing numbers on the path.

4. Write the missing numbers on the jam jars.

21   31   41   51   61   71

Section 1 — Numbers

Counting in 2s, 3s, 5s and 10s

5. Six of these ice creams have been joined to make a number pattern.
   Draw lines to add the other ice creams in the right order.

6. Fill in the two missing numbers in this sequence.

60   63   66   [69]   [72]   75

7. Two of the numbers in this pattern are wrong. Circle them.

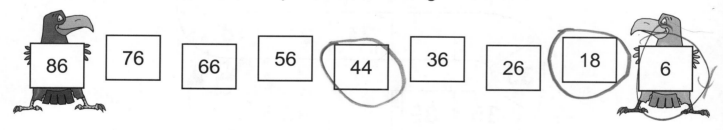

86   76   66   56   (44)   36   26   (18)   6

8. Fill in the three missing numbers below.

65   70   75   80   85   90   95   100

Are you happy with counting?

Number Lines

1. Fill in the missing number.

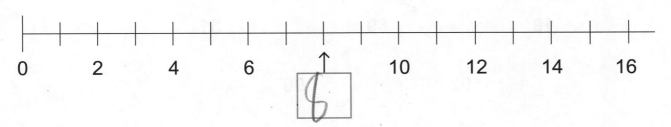

0   2   4   6   ↑   10   12   14   16

8

2. What number is the arrow pointing to on this number line?

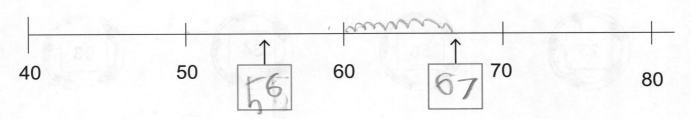

20   30   ↑   40   50   60

35

3. **Estimate** the numbers that the arrows are pointing to.

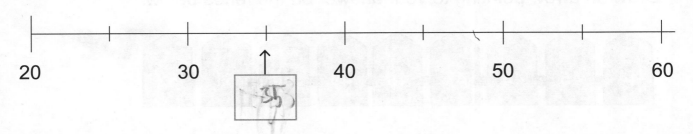

40   50   ↑   60   ↑ 70   80

56   67

4. Look at the sum in the box.

12 + 6

Draw an arrow pointing to its answer on the number line.

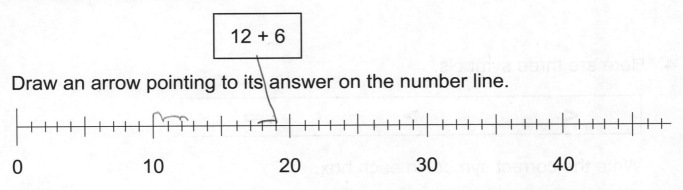

0   10   20   30   40

Are you bouncing like a Reasoning Roo?

Comparing Numbers

1. Circle the number that is **one less** than **91**.

   18   89   81

            92   90

2. Which number is **one more** than **49**?
   Draw an arrow pointing to your answer on the fence below.

   44 45 46 47 48 49 50 51 52

3. Draw lines to match each set of words with the correct football.

   23   56   34   98

   **equal to   less than   more than   one more than
   fifty-six   twenty-four   ninety   thirty-three**

4. Here are three symbols.

<	>	=

   Write the correct symbol in each box.

   53 [ ] 51   19 [ ] 19   86 [ ] 91

Comparing Numbers

5. Three friends are playing a game. Their scores are shown below.

   Put a **tick** next to the person with the **most** points.
   Put a **cross** next to the person with the **least** points.

Name	Points
John	59
Tamir	67
Ellie	62

6. Draw an arrow pointing to the number that is **three less** than **37**.

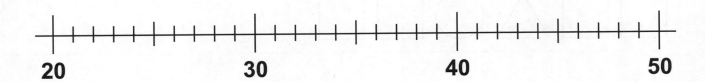

20   **30**   **40**   **50**

7. Tick **all** the number sentences that are correct.

   2 + 3 > 5   ☐   1 + 6 < 2 + 4   ☐

   4 − 2 = 2   ☐   5 + 1 > 6 − 2   ☐

Have you been leaping through this topic? ✓ ✓ ✓

 # Ordering and Patterns

1. Four children had a competition to see who could score the **most** goals.

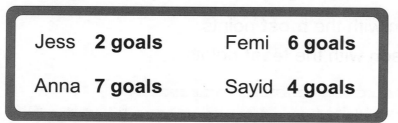

| Jess | **2 goals** | Femi | **6 goals** |
| Anna | **7 goals** | Sayid | **4 goals** |

Who came **second**?

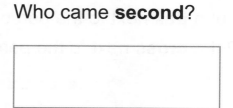

2. Write these numbers in order starting with the **smallest**.

| **34** | **73** | **28** | **88** | **82** | **37** |

3. Draw the next **four** shapes in the sequence.

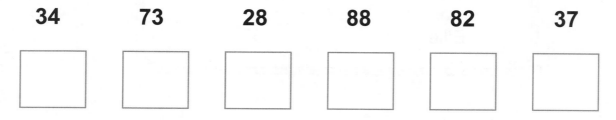

4. Look at this sequence.

Circle the triangle that comes **next** in the sequence.

Are you jumping like a Reasoning Roo?

Odd and Even Numbers

1. Write down **all** of the odd numbers that are **bigger than five** but **less than twelve**.

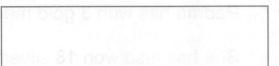

2. Here are some number cards.

Use these cards to make two different **even** numbers with **two digits**.

3. Colour in all of the **even** numbers in this sequence.

| 15 | 18 | 21 | 24 | 27 | 30 | 33 | 36 |

4. Write the numbers in the correct boxes. One has been done for you.

odd numbers		even numbers
11		

Are you happy like a Reasoning Roo?

Adding and Subtracting Problems

1. Padma has won **3** gold medals.

   She has also won **18** silver medals.

   How many medals has Padma won **altogether**?

	medals

2. There are **56** flowers in Anita's garden.

   30 of the flowers are **red**. The rest are yellow.

   How many **yellow** flowers are there?

	yellow flowers

3. Adam has **22** books on one shelf.

   He has **16** books on another shelf.

   How many books does Adam have in **total**?

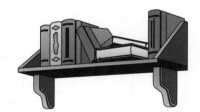

	books

4. Here is a calculation.

   > 55 – 30

   Circle **all** the calculations that have the **same answer** as the one in the box.

   30 – 55   35 – 10

   65 – 40   43 – 20

   35 – 20

Adding and Subtracting Problems

5. Qasim uses **37** bricks to build a tower.

   He has **40** bricks left over.

   How many bricks does he have **altogether**?

bricks

6. Dan and Harry each have **9** toy animals.

   Inga has **3** toy animals.

   How many toy animals do Dan, Harry and Inga have **altogether**?

animals

7. Draw a line to match the two calculations that have the **same** answer.

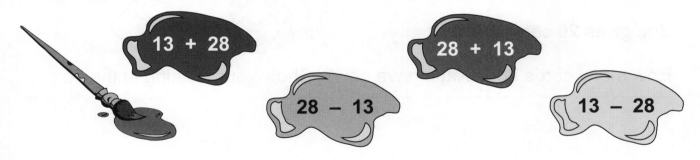

8. There are **64** apples on a tree.

   28 apples fall onto the ground.

   How many apples are **left** on the tree?

apples

Adding and Subtracting Problems

9. There are **20** people in a swimming pool.

    42 more people get in the pool.

    7 people get out of the pool.

    How many people are in the pool now? Show your working in the box.

people

10. Katie has **50** cards.

    She gives **18** cards to Greg.

    She gives **20** cards to Max.

    How many cards does Katie have now? Show your working in the box.

cards

Have you hopped through this topic?

Missing Number Problems

1. **Marta** gives **7** biscuits to Tim.

   Now **Marta** has **6** biscuits.

   How many biscuits did **Marta** have to begin with?

	biscuits

2. **18** of Beth's sandcastles have fallen down.

   13 of her sandcastles are still standing.

   How many sandcastles did Beth make?

	sandcastles

3. **58** children each have a pudding at lunch.

   8 teachers also have a pudding.

   There are **10** puddings left.

   How many puddings were there at the start of lunch?

	puddings

Are you bouncing like a Reasoning Roo?

Checking

1. Look at this subtraction.

26 – 3 = 23

    Circle the calculation that you could use to check the answer.

    3 – 23   3 + 26   23 + 3   3 – 26

2. Seb is doing a sum.

16 + 60 = 76

    Fill in the boxes to make **two** ways that Seb can check his answer.

76	–		=	16

76	–		=	

3. Look at the calculation in the cloud.

    Tick **two** calculations that can be used to **check** the answer.

    27 + 66

    93 – 27   66 – 27

    27 – 66   93 – 66 = 27   27 – 93

Can you check like a Reasoning Roo?

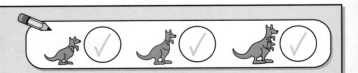

Multiplying and Dividing Problems

1. Here are Bonnie's toy boats.

Bonnie puts her boats into **6** equal groups.

How many boats are there in each group?

boats

2. Aidan is making **9** pots of soup.

He needs **2** onions for each pot.

How many onions does Aidan need **altogether**?

onions

3. There are **35** fish in a pet shop.

They are shared equally between **5** tanks.

How many fish are there in each tank?

fish

Section 1 — Numbers

 Multiplying and Dividing Problems

4. Nizar played **6** football games this year.

    He scored **3** goals in each game.

    Tick **two** calculations that will give the total number of goals Nizar scored.

    6 + 6 + 6 + 6 + 6 + 6   ☐      6 × 3   ☐

    3 + 3 + 3 + 3 + 3 + 3   ☐   3 + 6   ☐

5. Fill in the missing number to complete this number sentence.

    5   ×   10   =   10   ×   ☐

6. A bus has **10** rows of seats.

    Each row has **4** seats in it.

    How many seats are there in the bus in **total**?

seats

7. Lily runs **5** races every month.

    How many months will it take her to run **30** races?

months

Multiplying and Dividing Problems

8. Tick the truck that has two calculations with the **same answer**.

16 ÷ 2   2 ÷ 16

16 × 2   2 × 16

9. Alex has **8** balls.

   Ming has **10** balls.

   They put all their balls together and share them equally between **2** buckets.

   How many balls are there in each bucket?

   Show your working in the box.

balls

Have you been leaping through this topic?

Section 2 — Fractions

Halves

1. Put a tick next to **all** the pictures that show **half** of a pizza.

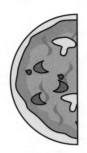  

2. Half of a rectangle has been drawn on this grid. Draw the other half.

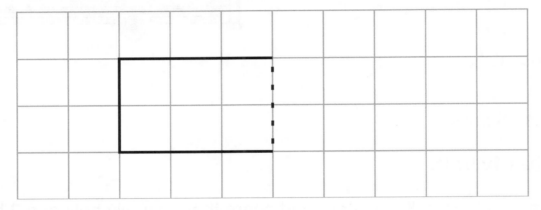

3. Circle $\frac{1}{2}$ of the marbles.

4. Feng has some stamps. He uses **half** of the stamps.

   There are **four** stamps left.

   How many stamps did Feng have to start with?

   | stamps |

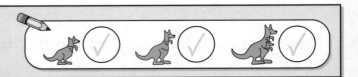

Have you got the hang of halves?

Thirds

1. Shade $\frac{1}{3}$ of each shape.

2. Emma's mum cuts a sandwich into **three** equal pieces.

    Emma eats **one** piece.

    What fraction of the sandwich does she eat?

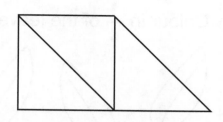

3. Draw lines to match each **fraction problem** with its **answer.**

$\frac{1}{3}$ of 30

$\frac{1}{3}$ of 9

$\frac{1}{3}$ of 12

3

4

10

4. Rose collects **6** pebbles.

    She puts **one third** of her pebbles in a pot.

    How many pebbles does she put in the pot?

pebbles

Are you happy like a Reasoning Roo?

Quarters

1. Colour in $\frac{1}{4}$ of the leaves.

2. A fraction of each shape has been **shaded**.

    Draw lines to match each shape with the correct **fraction**
    and the correct **words**.

    $\frac{3}{4}$  **one quarter**

    $\frac{1}{4}$ 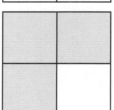 **three quarters**

3. There is a **fraction problem** on the side of each chest.

    Colour in the number inside the chest that gives the **answer**.

Quarters

4. There are **20** horses in a field.

   One quarter of the horses are brown.

   How many brown horses are there?

brown horses

5. Tick **two** sentences that are correct.

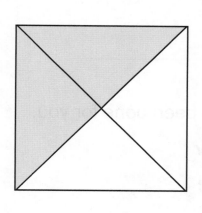

$\frac{1}{2}$ of the square is grey. ☐

$\frac{1}{3}$ of the square is grey. ☐

$\frac{2}{4}$ of the square is grey. ☐

$\frac{3}{4}$ of the square is grey. ☐

6. Fill in the missing numbers on the number line.

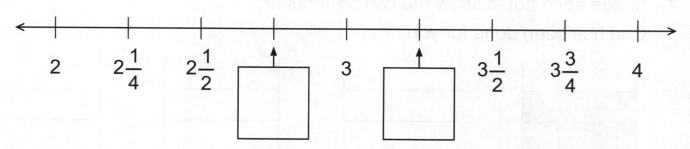

2    $2\frac{1}{4}$ $2\frac{1}{2}$ ☐   3   ☐ $3\frac{1}{2}$ $3\frac{3}{4}$ 4

Have you hopped through this topic?

Section 3 — Measurement

Different Amounts

1. Circle the **heaviest** object.

2. Draw a **longer** fish in the box.

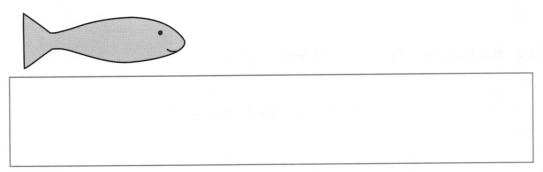

3. Draw lines to match the **opposite** words. One has been done for you.

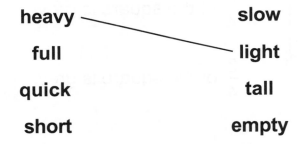

4. Shade each pot to show the correct amount.
   One has been done for you.

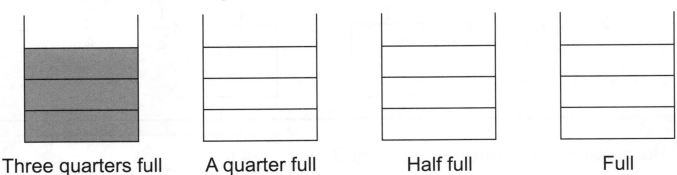

Three quarters full   A quarter full   Half full   Full

Different Amounts

5. Circle **earlier** or **later** to make each sentence correct.

   Joe arrives **before** Lucy. Joe arrives **earlier** / **later** than Lucy.

   Mike arrives **after** Lucy. Mike arrives **earlier** / **later** than Lucy.

6. Match each object to the correct description. One has been done for you.

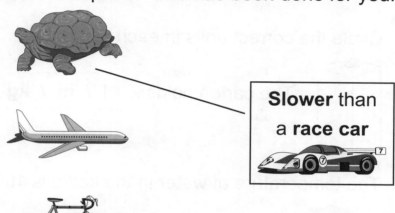

7. Tick the correct boxes.

Which train carriage is **double** the **length** of the other?

Which bookcase is **half** the **height** of the other?

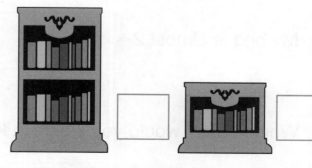

Are you happy like a Reasoning Roo?

Units

1. Match the **units** to the things they **measure**. One has been done for you.

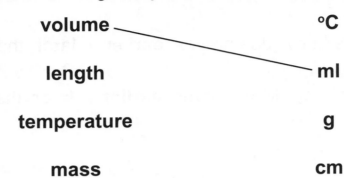

volume ——————— °C

length ————— ml

temperature   g

mass   cm

2. Circle the correct units in each sentence.

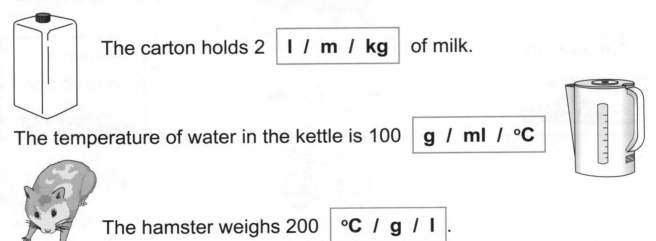

The carton holds 2 | **l / m / kg** | of milk.

The temperature of water in the kettle is 100 | **g / ml / °C** |

The hamster weighs 200 | **°C / g / l** |.

3. Fill each gap with something from the circle.

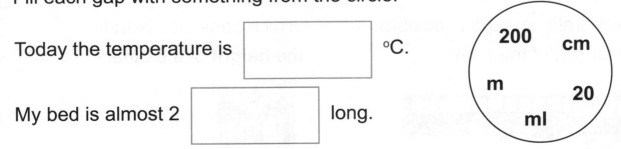

Today the temperature is [   ] °C.

My bed is almost 2 [   ] long.

200   cm

m

20

ml

4. Which object would you weigh in **kilograms**? Circle your answer.

Units

5. Write the correct unit for each picture. Choose from the options.

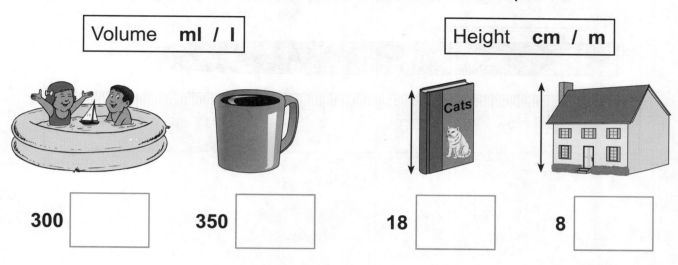

| Volume   **ml / l** |

| Height   **cm / m** |

300 ☐   350 ☐   18 ☐   8 ☐

6. For each pair of measurements, circle the one that is **smaller**.

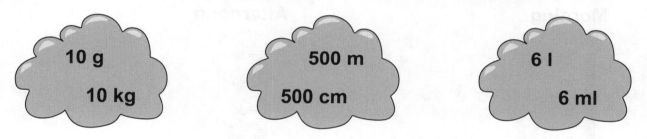

10 g
10 kg

500 m
500 cm

6 l
6 ml

7. Write the correct units next to each measuring tool.
    One has been done for you.

| g   ml   °C   c̶m̶ |

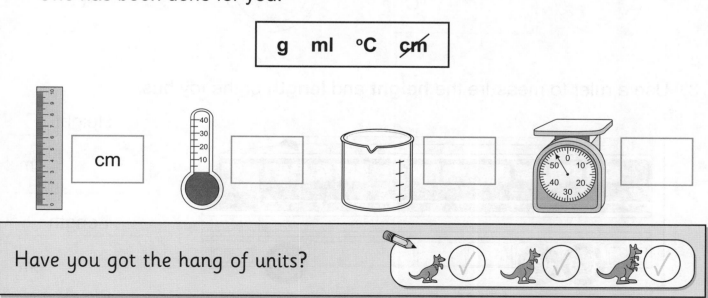

cm

Have you got the hang of units?

Measuring

1. How long is the pen?

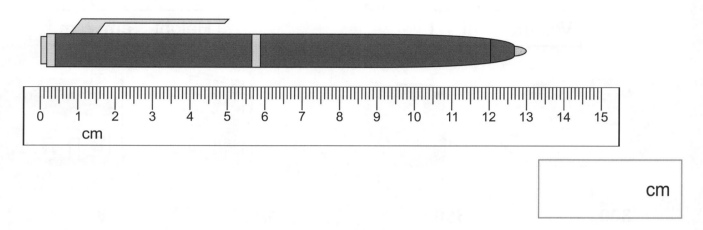

cm

2. Tommy is measuring the temperature outside.
   What is the temperature in the **morning** and in the **afternoon**?

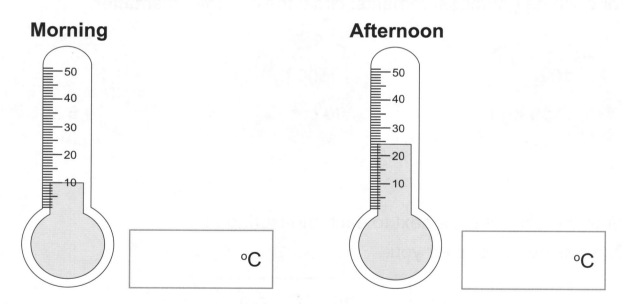

Morning

°C

Afternoon

°C

3. Use a ruler to measure the **height** and **length** of the toy bus.

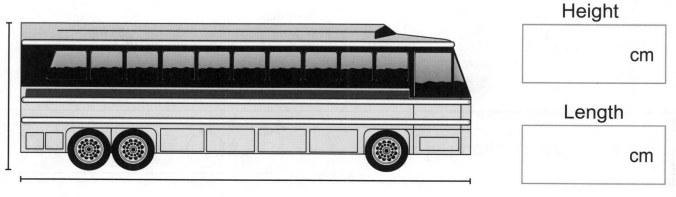

Height

cm

Length

cm

Measuring

4. How much does the mouse weigh?

grams

5. Colour in these pots to show the correct volumes.

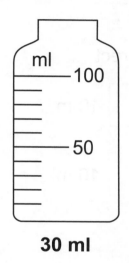

30 ml

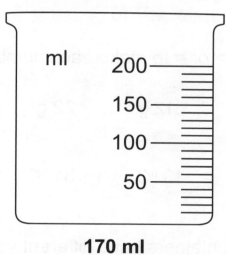

170 ml

6. Draw the weight of each item on the scales.

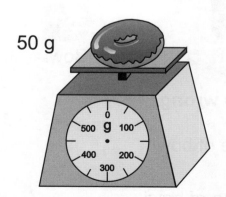

50 g

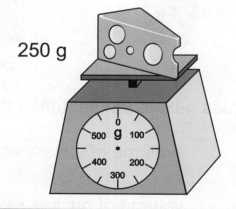

250 g

Are you bouncing like a Reasoning Roo?

Comparing Measurements

1. Yasmin's teddy weighs **600 g**.

   Her doll weighs **1 kg**.

   Tick the see-saw that shows the teddy and doll in the correct places.

2. Write **<**, **>** or **=** to make each number sentence correct.

   12 g ☐ 22 g   16 m ☐ 10 m

   13 °C ☐ 31 °C   10 ml ☐ 10 ml

3. These containers have different volumes.

   5 l   **10 l**   **2 l**

   Vase   Bucket   Bowl

   Put a cross next to the sentence that is **wrong**.

   volume of vase > volume of bowl   ☐

   volume of bucket > volume of bowl   ☐

   volume of bucket < volume of vase   ☐

Comparing Measurements

4. Put these lengths in order from **shortest** to **longest**.

   1 m   20 m   2 m   120 m   10 m

   Shortest   Longest

5. A postman has these parcels.

   He puts all the parcels that weigh **more than 2 kg** in his van.

   Circle all the parcels that he puts in his van.

   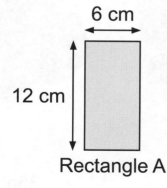   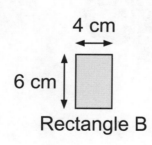      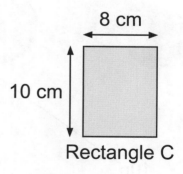

   500 g   3 kg   4 kg   1 kg

6. Look at the rectangles below.

   6 cm

   12 cm   Rectangle A

   4 cm

   6 cm   Rectangle B

   8 cm

   10 cm   Rectangle C

   Which rectangle is **half as tall** as **Rectangle A**?

Rectangle

   Which rectangle is **twice as wide** as **Rectangle B**?

Rectangle

   Can you compare like a Reasoning Roo?

Section 3 — Measurement

Money

1. Join these coins in order from the **smallest value** to the **largest value**.

2. Circle the coins that are worth **more than 5p**.

3. Draw lines to match the coins with the value they add up to.
   One has been done for you.

   10p   £2   40p   35p

4. Jade uses these coins to pay for a puzzle that costs **65p**.

   How much **change** does she get?

p

Money

5. Sana makes **60p** with **two** coins. Draw **circles** around the coins she uses.

   Mo makes **60p** with **four** coins. Draw **squares** around the coins he uses.

6. Jack buys this pencil.  48p

   The shopkeeper gives him this change.

   How much money did Jack give the shopkeeper?

p

7. Will has these coins.

   He wants to buy **one** piece of fruit.

   Which two fruits can he choose from?
   Tick the fruits on the list.

Apple.................30p

Banana...............12p

Pear...................37p

Melon.................70p

Money

8. The tooth fairy gives **10p** for every tooth that falls out.

   Luke has lost **three** teeth.

   How much money has Luke been given by the tooth fairy?

   | | p |

9. Kimmy buys a notebook and a rubber. She spends **67p** in total.

   A notebook costs **50p**.

   What is the price of a rubber?

   | | p |

10. Peter spends **34p** on some sweets.

    He pays with a **50p** coin.

    Complete the calculation to find Peter's change.

    50p − [p] = [p]

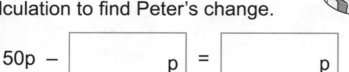

11. Sid's mum and dad give her some money.

    | Mum **50p** | Dad **20p** |

    A ball costs **90p**.

    How much **more** money does Sid need to buy the ball?

    | | p |

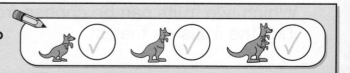

Have you been leaping through this topic?

Days and Months

1. Circle the days that are **weekend days**.

   Wednesday   Sunday   Monday   Thursday

   Tuesday   Friday   Saturday

2. Fill in the gaps to write the **months** of the year in order.

   January   February      April   May 

   July   September   October   November   December

3. Hana has her violin lesson on **Monday morning**.

   Matt has his violin lesson on **Monday afternoon**.

   Circle **before** or **after** to make this sentence correct.

    Hana has her lesson   **before** / **after**   Matt.

4. Circle the answer to each question.

   How many days are there in **July**?

        30   29   28   31

   How many days are there in a **year**?

        365   7   300   12

           Section 3 — Measurement

Days and Months

5. If today is **Thursday**, what day was it **yesterday**?

   If today is **Saturday**, what day is **next** in the week?

6. How many **days** are there in **10** weeks?

   days

   How many **months** are there in **2** years?

   months

7. The table shows some children's names and the months of their birthdays.

Name	Birthday month
Ava	March
Pari	
Bill	

   Use these clues to complete the table.

   Clue 1: **Pari's** birthday is in the month **after Ava's**.

   Clue 2: **Bill's** birthday is in the **first month of the year**.

Are you happy with days and months?

Time

1. Put a tick below the clock that shows the time **twenty past nine**.

2. Write the times shown on these clocks.

[ ] past [ ]   [ ] to [ ]

3. Draw hands on the clock faces to show these times.

Five o'clock

Quarter to ten

Twenty-five to eleven

 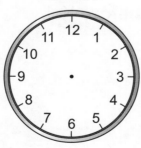 

4. Fill in the gaps in these sentences.

There are [ ] **hours** in a **day**.

There are [ ] **minutes** in an **hour**.

Section 3 — Measurement

Time

5. Adam and Ben write down the times they take to colour in 3 pictures.

   Cross out the **slower** time for each picture.

Picture 1	Picture 2	Picture 3
Adam **13 minutes**	Adam **1 minute**	Adam **45 minutes**
Ben **3 minutes**	Ben **50 seconds**	Ben **1 hour**

6. Tyrone and Aya have the same jigsaw.

   These were the times it took them to finish it.

Tyrone **14 minutes 30 seconds**	Aya **14 minutes 10 seconds**

   Circle the correct word in each sentence.

   Tyrone was **quicker** / **slower** than Aya.

   Aya finished the jigsaw **first** / **last.**

7. Kai arrives at school at **half past eight**.

   Omar and Ruby arrive at these times.

   Tick the person who arrives **before** Kai.

   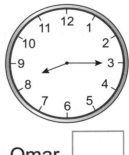

   Omar [ ]   Ruby [ ]

8. Jay is doing his homework.

   He **starts** at this time.

   He **finishes** at this time.

   How long does Jay spend doing his homework?   [ ] minutes

Time

9. Nia, Finn and Charlie ran in a race. These were their times.

   Write **1st**, **2nd**, or **3rd** next to their names to show where they came in the race.

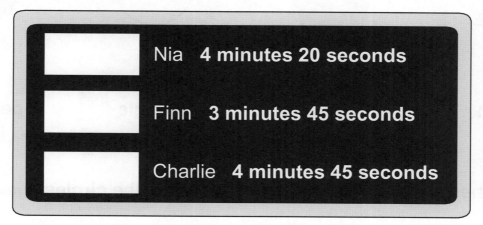

Nia   4 minutes 20 seconds

Finn   3 minutes 45 seconds

Charlie   4 minutes 45 seconds

10. Sophie's favourite TV programme starts at **5 o'clock**.

    It lasts **twenty minutes**.

    Draw hands on the clock to show when it finishes.

11. Some cyclists took part in a race. These were their times.

    Put a **tick** under the **fastest** cyclist. Put a **cross** under the **slowest** cyclist.

52 minutes
13 seconds

52 minutes
5 seconds

1 hour
4 seconds

56 minutes
11 seconds

Are you jumping like a Reasoning Roo?

Section 4 — Geometry

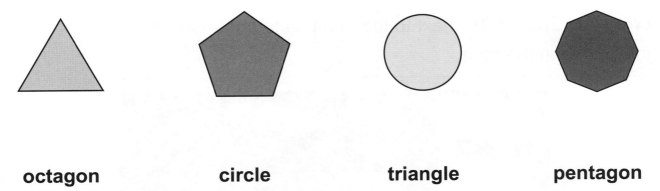

2D Shapes

1. Draw lines to match each shape with the correct name.

octagon **circle** **triangle** **pentagon**

2. Look at these objects. Put a tick under each of the **circles**.

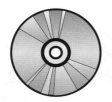    

3. Draw lines to match each shape with the correct **group**.
   One has been done for you.

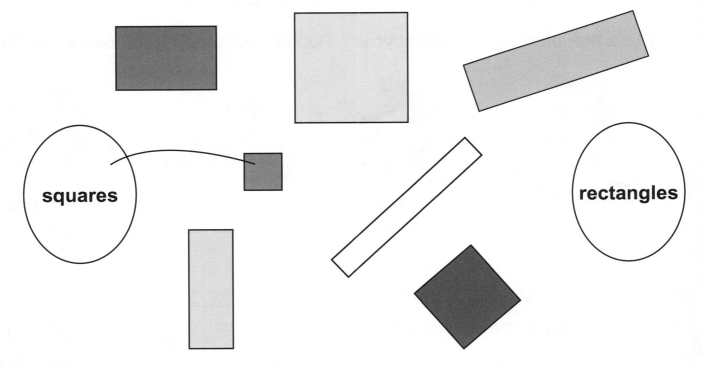

squares **rectangles**

2D Shapes

4. Match the name of each shape with the correct number of **sides**.

pentagon	3
triangle	6
hexagon	4
square	5

5. Cross out all of the shapes that are **not hexagons**.

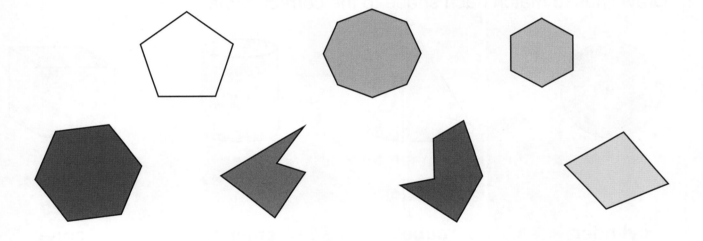

6. Draw **one line of symmetry** on each of these shapes.

Are you happy with 2D shapes?

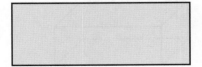

Section 4 — Geometry

3D Shapes

1. Draw a ring around all the objects that are **cuboids**.

2. Draw lines to match each shape to the correct name.

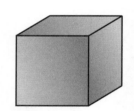

cylinder   **cube**   **sphere**   **cone**

3. How many **faces** does each shape have?

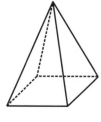
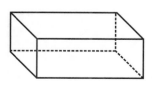
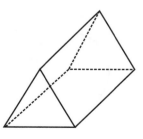

3D Shapes

4. Draw lines to match each shape with the correct number of **edges**.

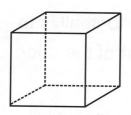 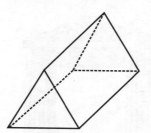 

9 edges   **2 edges**   **12 edges**

5. Tick the shape that has **5 vertices**.

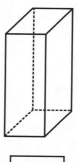 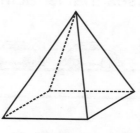 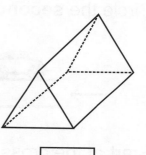

6. Look at this 3D shape.

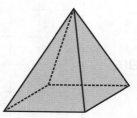

Draw a ring around **two** shapes that make up its **faces**.

hexagon   **circle**

pentagon   **square**   **triangle**

Have you got the hang of 3D shapes?

Position and Directions

1. Draw lines to match each sentence with the correct football in the picture.

The football is **behind** the door.

The football is **in front** of the door.

The football is **above** the door.

The football is **between** the doors.

2. Demi walks along the pavement in the direction of the arrow.

Circle the **second car** she passes that is facing **forwards**.

3. Start at the cross and move forwards in the direction of the arrow. Then follow these instructions.

Turn **left** at the **circle**.

Move **forwards** until you are **between** two triangles.

Turn **right** and move **forwards**.

Draw a ring around the **first shape** you reach.

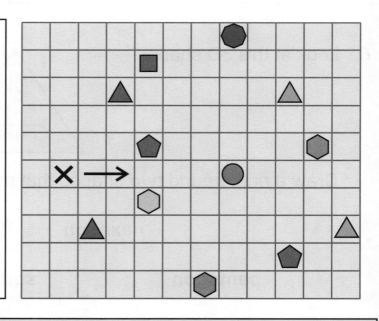

Are you jumping like a Reasoning Roo?

Turns

1. Draw the spinner arrow after it has made a **half turn**.

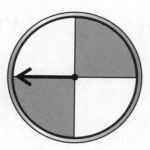

2. The bat makes a **three-quarter** turn **anti-clockwise**.

   Tick the box that shows the direction the bat faces **after** the turn.

3. Here is a steering wheel.

   It is rotated through **one right angle** turn **clockwise**.

   Circle the picture that shows the steering wheel **after** it has been rotated.

Section 4 — Geometry

Turns

4. Tick the **three** options that describe how the shape has been **rotated**.

Before rotation   **After rotation**

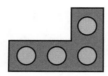   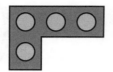

| | quarter turn anti-clockwise | | | half turn anti-clockwise |

| | two right angle turns clockwise | | | half turn clockwise |

| | three-quarter turn clockwise | | | four right angle turns |

5. Circle the correct **instruction** in each sentence
    to help the rocket to get to the planet.

1) Go forward 3 squares, then do a
   quarter / half turn clockwise.

2) Go forward **4 / 5** squares.

3) Do one right angle turn
   clockwise / anti-clockwise,
   then go forward 3 squares.

4) Do a **quarter / three-quarter** turn
   anti-clockwise and go forward 1 square.

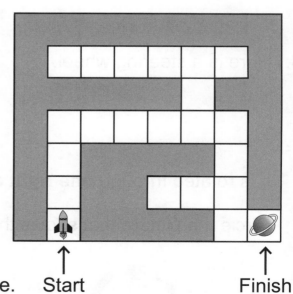

Start   Finish

Can you do turns like a Reasoning Roo?

Tables

1. This table shows the games some children like to play.

	Abby	Noah	Ali	Iba
Game	⚽	🪢	🎾	🪢

Who likes to play tennis?

How many children like skipping? [ ] children

2. This table shows some children's **favourite** and **least favourite** fruits.

	Eve	Reece	Laura	Toby
Favourite fruit	apple	orange	apple	apple
Least favourite fruit	banana	apple	orange	

How many children said **apples** are their favourite fruit? [ ] children

Toby's **least favourite** fruit is the **same** as Eve's. Draw this in the table.

3. This table shows some children's ages.

Tick the **oldest** child.

Circle the **youngest** child.

Name	Age
Rima	6
Imran	7
Rob	4

Tables

4. This table shows the number of acorns Lena collected on four days.

	Thursday	Friday	Saturday	Sunday
Number of acorns	5	8		7

These are the acorns Lena collected on **Saturday**.
Use this information to fill the gap in the table.

How many acorns did Lena collect on **Sunday**?

acorns

5. Milly asked her friends to name their favourite colour.
   4 said **blue**, **6** said **pink** and **2** said **red**.

   Put this information into the table below.

Colour	Number of friends

6. This table shows how the children in Class 2 travel to school.

	Walking	Bus	Car
Number of children	9	4	8

How many **more** children travel in a **car** than on a **bus**?

children

How many children are there **altogether** in Class 2?

children

Are you terrific at tables?

Tally Charts

1. Write the number of tally marks in the boxes.

||| [ ]   卌 |||| [ ]

卌 卌 ||| [ ]   卌 卌 卌 || [ ]

2. Aysha makes a tally chart of the food in a shopping bag.

Food	Tally
	||
YOGHURT	卌
(bread)	|||

Circle the correct number of each type of food. One has been done for you.

3. This tally chart shows what some children did on Saturday.
   3 children went to the **seaside**, **7** went to the **park** and **2** went to a **funfair**.

   Complete the tally chart to show this.

Activity	Number of children
Seaside	|||
Park	
Funfair	

Tally Charts

4. The tally chart shows the animals that the children in Year 2 chose to draw.

Animal	Tally
Monkey	卌 IIII
Horse	卌 卌 II
Giraffe	III

Which animal did the **fewest** children draw?

How many **more** children drew a **horse** than a **monkey**? children

5. This tally chart shows the towns where the children in Leah's class live.
   Fill in the missing boxes.

Town	Tally	Total
Moorfield	卌 卌	10
Westside	卌 卌 IIII	
Newton		6

6. Cody asked some friends whether they prefer singing or dancing.
   Fill in the **total** column in his tally chart.

	Tally	Total
Singing	IIII	
Dancing	卌 III	

How many friends did Cody ask **altogether**? friends

Have you hopped through this topic?

Block Diagrams

1. This block diagram shows some children's favourite cereals.

   Put a **tick** below the **most popular** cereal.

   Put a **cross** below the **least popular** cereal.

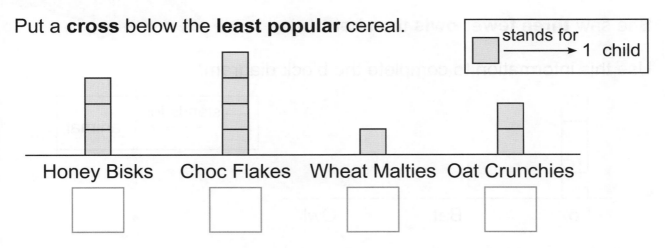

2. This block diagram shows the vehicles on a street.
   Write the **number** of each vehicle under its name.
   One has been done for you.

Car	Lorry	Van	Bus	Motorbike
3				

3. This table shows the colours of the crayons in a pack.
   Use the table to finish the block diagram.

Colour	Number of crayons
Red	5
Green	3
Blue	4

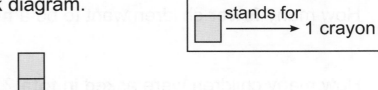

Block Diagrams

4. Sonya is making a block diagram to show the animals she sees at night.

   She saw the **same number** of **bats** as **foxes**.

   She saw **three fewer owls** than **bats**.

   Use this information to complete the block diagram.

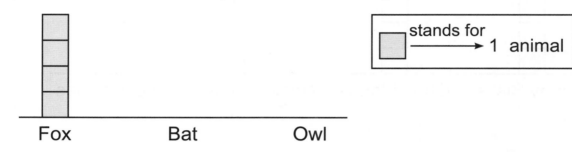

5. Some children were asked what they want to be when they grow up.
   The block diagram shows the results.

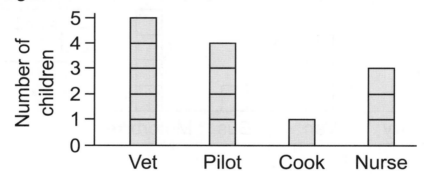

   How many **more** children want to be a **pilot** than a **cook**? [ ] children

   How many **fewer** children want to be a **nurse** than a **vet**? [ ] children

   How many children were asked in **total**? [ ] children

Are you bouncing like a Reasoning Roo?

Pictograms

1. This pictogram shows how many letters arrived at Tia's house over 4 days.

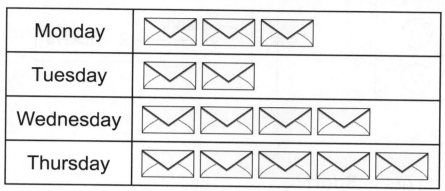

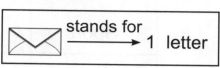

How many letters arrived on **Monday**? [   ] letters

On which day did the **fewest** letters arrive? Tick the correct answer.

Monday [   ]   Tuesday [   ]   Wednesday [   ]   Thursday [   ]

How many letters arrived in **total**? [   ] letters

2. Harvey helps his mum to plant some flowers in the garden.
    He makes this pictogram to show their colours.

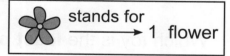

How many **more blue** flowers than
pink flowers do they plant?   [   ] blue flowers

They plant **4 orange** flowers. Show this on the pictogram.

Pictograms

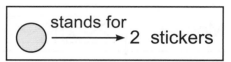

3. This pictogram shows how many stickers Li gets in 3 lessons at school.

Sport	◯ ◯
Music	◯ ◯ ◖
Art	

◯ stands for → 2 stickers

How many stickers did Li get in **Sport**? ☐ stickers

Li got **3** stickers in **Art**. Show this on the pictogram.

How many **fewer** stickers did Li get in **Art** than in **Music**? ☐ stickers

4. Some children were asked what their favourite toy is.
   This pictogram shows the results.

Doll	▢ ▢ ▢
Teddy	▢ ▢
Scooter	▢ ▢ ▟

▢ stands for → 4 children

Which toy is the **least popular**? ☐

How many children said their favourite toy is a **doll**? ☐ children

How many **more** children said their favourite toy is a **scooter** than a **teddy**? ☐ children